LUCENT – An ode to Nan Shepherd's
The Living Mountain

Published by
8d Press, Fife Scotland – June 2021
Copyright is held by individual authors

ISBN: 978-0-9935424-8-0

www.8dpress.co.uk
hello@8dpress.co.uk

Compiled and edited by Jo Chumas

Designed and typeset by Lucy Arbuthnott
Lucy Designs, Dunfermline, Fife
Text in Book Antiqua font
www.lucydesigns.co.uk

Printed by the Pureprint Group, UK
www.pureprint.co.uk in England
On 100gsm Munken Lynx Rough Natural White
Cover 150gsm White Silk Art mounted over
3mm Grey board
End papers are Colourplan Azure Blue 120gsm

World Land Trust approved

WORLD
LAND
TRUST™
www.carbonbalancedpaper.com
CBP00019082504183028

LUCENT

An ode to Nan Shepherd's
The Living Mountain

A limited print edition of 500 numbered and dated copies

NEW SCOTTISH WRITING

LUCENT

An ode to Nan Shepherd's
The Living Mountain

With a Foreword by Professor Sir Geoff Palmer,
Chancellor of Heriot-Watt University,
Edinburgh, Scotland

Compiled and edited by Jo Chumas

AN ANTHOLOGY OF WOMEN WRITERS

8d

Foreword
Professor Sir Geoff Palmer CA
Renowned scientist, human rights' activist and
Chancellor of Heriot-Watt University, Edinburgh

My genes say that I am from Africa and
Scotland – indeed I have some Viking in
me - but I was born in Jamaica, an island
which has long historical connections
with Scotland. The flags of Jamaica
and Scotland have similar designs but
different colours.

Nature also has different colours that
we love. The welcoming, calming effect
of Scotland is celebrated in these lovely
poems and short pieces that were a delight
to read.

This love letter to Scotland is a celebration
of Scottish nature writer Nan Shepherd

and contains love expressed in prose and poetry.

It sings with sensual experiences; poetry about wild-flowers such as heather and broom sweeping over Scottish hills, where birds sing and rivers run into multi-coloured seas. The hills of the Highlands are brimming with the sensuality of nature, as are the lakes full to the brim with clear clean water.

Like Scotland's Great Tapestry, diversity in culture is sewn in every thread. I have had the great honour of stitching some of these threads in my life as a Jamaican-Scots scientist.

LUCENT paints a wonderful picture of Scotland, a country which says welcome 'we are different but the same', and it was such a comfort to read. I live between the Pentland Hills and

the Lothian Esk river and, in between
our small towns, are fields of sheep
and cows.

Some days the hills can be covered with
snow or sunshine or both. Birds of all
kinds, from small songbirds to large
seagulls fly and feed together.

The gulls of Bass Rock are mentioned and
I recognised my own roaming seagull,
who I call Gilbert and who has been
visiting my 'equality garden', where all
animals are equal, for many, many years.

As I read this thoughtful book of life
experiences, I recalled the many trips I
have made in Scotland, form the East to
the West and from the Lowlands to the
Highlands to give lectures on Scottish-
Caribbean history and malting barley.

A love for Scotland is embodied in this
eloquent book of prose, poetry and short

stories. It will stand the test of time in what it hopes to achieve; an ode to nature, an ode to the sensuality of Scotland and a picture of who we are as a people.

Edinburgh
June 2021

Dedication

LUCENT is dedicated to our friend
Polly Plouviez who introduced us
to Nan Shepherd and her book
The Living Mountain.

Introduction

A Love Letter to Scotland

By Jo Chumas, Founder of 8d Press

I fell in love with Scotland back in 1981 when I first visited the Edinburgh Festival with my parents. I was an anxious unruly teenager at the time, brought in from the European city of Brussels, desperate to break away from my parents. As soon as we arrived in Edinburgh my anxiety settled down and my curiosity swung into overdrive.

What was this strange, mysterious place we were visiting? Why did the sight of the historic buildings fill me with joy? What was it about Edinburgh and Scotland that made me feel so at home? I couldn't answer any of those questions, but one thing was certain, I knew one day I would return.

And I did. Back in 1991 to work and find myself. It was in Edinburgh that summer that my first piece of writing was published, and so the love affair was sealed as something for eternity.

When I was introduced to Nan Shepherd's *The Living Mountain* I felt this renewed sense of wonder and awe; the beauty of her language in describing the effect nature was having on her back in the post-World War Two years made me cry out in recognition. Here was my Scotland, on the page in front of me.

As a writer and publisher I knew I had to publish an ode to Nan Shepherd, and how Scotland makes me feel, as a resident, as a fan, as an inquisitive type, and so here it is; twenty-two amazing encounters, courtesy of twenty-two amazing women writers who love Scotland as much as I do. These women writers come from all backgrounds, reiterating just how welcoming and diverse Scotland truly is, and how it has become a home to the many. As a former third culture child bought up 'all over the place' finding a home in Scotland was always important to me.

LUCENT represents glittering hope in these dark Covid and post-Covid times. We hope you enjoy our ode to the sensuality present everywhere in Scotland if you choose to look.

Dunfermline
Fife
Scotland
June 2021

LIBERTY

Natalie Jayne Clark

Natalie Jayne Clark is a neurodivergent writer, editor and teacher based in Perth, Scotland.

She is a part of *The Scribbler's Union* writers' collective and regularly performs at spoken-word events and competitions.

For Natalie, movement is magic - swimming in the river, walking or cycling along its banks, or dancing in the air on a pole or aerial hoop, amongst other bodily activities.

Her inspiration for this collection came from the feeling of nature on her skin and the absorbing adoring language about it in Nan Shepherd's *The Living Mountain*. She owes a credit to Kevin P. Gilday and Imogen Stirling for giving her the tools to express her relationship with the natural world in poetic form.

Hill Walking in Summer

*d*electable as honey
a roaring scourge
both are part of its essential
nature
I am seeking knowledge
a process of living
not done easily nor in an hour
a tale too slow for impatience

Yet it has its own rare value

One never quite knows
the mountain, nor
oneself in relation to it
However often I walk
on them, these hills
hold astonishment for me.

There is no getting accustomed to them.

After Nan Shepherd (found poetry from 'The Plateau' in 'The Living Mountain'), published by Canongate Books 2014.

~~Summer on the high plateau can be~~ delectable as honey; ~~it can also be~~ a roaring scourge. ~~To those who love the place, both are good, since~~ both are part of its essential nature. ~~And it is to know its essential nature that~~ I am seeking ~~here. To know, that is, with the~~ knowledge ~~that is~~ a process of living. ~~This is~~ not done easily nor in an hour. ~~It is~~ a tale too slow for ~~the~~ impatience ~~of our age, not of immediate enough import for its desperate problems.~~ Yet it has its own rare value. ~~It is, for one thing, a corrective of glib assessment:~~ one never quite knows the mountain, nor oneself in relation to it. However often I walk on them, these hills hold astonishment for me. There is no getting accustomed to them.

Go to the River Tay

There you will see rushing visions and
dreams
Made of ribbons and snakes, blue and
green
Folding and pushing and twisting
I n t e r t w i n i n g

There you will feel silky cool water
An al-fresco lover
They run their smooth hands up your
calves
Cupping your cheeks
Their fingers stroke up and down your
spine
And hold you tightly in between the thighs

There you will touch rough recondite rocks
Feel them scrape and caress the whorls of
your feet

You stand, proclaim, declare
And when you slip in your exuberance
You clutch, you dig your fingers into the
gaps and cracks
As if you wish to be absorbed into
Its mossy folds
Held fast for the rest
Of time

There you will lose the concept of
separation
You and your friends joined together, as
one
With and within this murky liquid
panacea

There, by the water's edge
You will find the best place to share and
sip steaming tea
The seat isn't comfy but the view is
unparalleled

What shall we call you, river that calls us always?

Don't call me river
Call me skin-stroker

Don't call me river
Call me music-maker

Don't call me river
Call me moon-mirror

Call me pallid-panacea
Call me bond-giver
Call me perspective-changer

Don't call me river
Call me soul-renewer

River Therapy

First in the stripping off
Displaying the lumps and bumps and
folds and scars
Eddies and tributaries
Watching the goosebumps grow

Then in the first shivering toe
It screams at you
But you soothe it gently and soon...

Soon, with water clawing your ankles
You fling your arms open to embrace the
corporeal wind
Displaying every single bit of you
To the world – this world here

After, cold squeezes your thighs, *firmly*

Until you brave the shove-dunk of the

shoulders under the water
That's the defining moment, the moment
where there is
   no
      going
           back

Head under, face bursting into the fresh
world
Underneath

Drawn up and out and that first breath
above is true and deep and new
Your first breath as the new you, the next
you

You who is one with this water
The chills have fled to be replaced by
certainty
Goose skin to selkie skin

Now, you are one to be seen

Standing and posing and proclaiming off
rocks

One last dive, one last pull by the river's
rope
One last flick of drips off fingertips and
hairtips

Before you must step out into sand
Stuck rough on your legs

Leave your hair uncombed and wet
To take all the living river home with you

THE DAWN

Jane Brydon

Jane is currently working with the Creative Scotland *Our Voices* development program on her novel which tells the story of a friendship between a nurse and a young woman with Down's Syndrome, inspired by her own career working with people with learning disabilities.

In October 2020 her short story *Tinned Secrets* was featured in a popular UK fiction magazine.

The Village of Magical Things

Hidden away beyond the roaring traffic of the motorway and rising up with great authority to 1538 feet above sea level, Wanlockhead proudly claims its title as the highest village in Scotland.

Winding along the curvaceous body of a road from Abington and through Leadhills, its imposing green and brown hills finally come into view.

In the short time since I made it my home, I have been mesmerized by the aura of the place with its sweeping moods.

Like an adolescent with scant control over the hormonal switches in their maturing body, the landscape alters hour by hour, so that one moment I am bathed in the glorious warm honey glow of sunshine peeking out from behind billowing white candy floss clouds and the next, I am shadowed by a circling swathe of dense grey mist threatening to burst forth a deluge of cold, thick, heavy rain with which to remind me who is in control.

There's a beauty in the stark grittiness of Wanlockhead that leaves me breathless.

As I walk along the stony paths, passing the skeletal remains of the old lead mining works which once dominated this small village, I think I hear the voices of the miners calling out through the fine silver mist, beckoning me back to days long gone.

There is a sense of calm here, and even when the gold panners in search of a rare nugget, descend upon the tributaries of running water that snake their way down the hills and through the village, I sense there is a respect for the spirits of those old mine workers, for the blood and sweat etched into every crevice of those old mines with their crumbling bricks and great rusting sheets of metal.

But beyond the harsh outlines of that forgotten industry, and the squat miniature houses lie the microcosm of life. The rivulets of water tracing their way down the hills, settle in deep pools in which tiny stars of vibrant green moss explode.

Once a year they fill with pearls of frogspawn, wriggling beneath the surface of the water until the frogs are ready to leap free.

Insects flitter past my face, some stopping to rest a while, to savour the taste of me. Tiny bank voles and stoats appear from holes and peek out, wondering who this interloper is, whilst a host of ravenous birds; finch, coal tits, blue tits, robins, and once the rare sight of a woodpecker, feast upon the seeds swaying softly on the bird feeder I've placed carefully in my range of sight.

Rabbits skitter about the hillside amongst curious sheep who go eagerly about their business of keeping the dense green grass clipped low.

Suddenly a rabbit darts beneath the ground, perhaps startled by the footfall of a rambler or the whisper of a raptor's wings.

Graceful birds somehow manage to ride the waves of the fiercest wind, wings outstretched, bodies taut, then plummet to the ground to seize their prey before rising again on a waft of air.

The grouse call and cackle amongst the purple heather, occasionally taking flight, and at dusk as the sun lights the sky in flames of deep pink, violet and orange, the owl sweeps across the flat land, resting on a fence post, staring with wide eyes, watching, waiting.

The ball of red-hot light finally sinks behind the hills. I shiver against the cold of the darkening sky and linger. Soon, the bats leave their resting place and flit before me in a magical dance of black wings.

I am but a temporary incomer to this village I know as home, a truly magical place.

Leela Soma

Leela Soma was born in Madras, India and now lives in Glasgow, Scotland.

Her poems and short stories have been published in several anthologies, and publications.

She has published three novels, short stories and two collections of poetry. Her poems have been published in *Gutter, The Blue Nib, Anthropocene, Black Bough Poems, The Glasgow Review of Books* and many others.

She was also was nominated for the *Pushcart Prize 2020*. She has been appointed *Scrivener 2021* for the Federation of Writers, Scotland. Some of her work reflects her dual heritage of India and Scotland.

Twitter: @glasgowlee
www.leelasoma.wordpress.com
Author of *Twice Born, Bombay Baby* and *Murder at the Mela.*

Burnished Gold

(Glasgow, autumn 1969)

*T*he gunmetal grey skies of autumn, oppressive and threatening to rain was the first striking image of my arriving at my new home, a young girl straight out of Madras to the first world.

A familiar world on pages of books we had read during our school days at Good Shepherd Convent.

It was rather different from what I had imagined.

The black taxi that took us home from the train station. The friendly taxi driver's words sounded like another language to me!

"Hey Jimmy," he says to my husband, "naw a great day eh? Looks like rain again, not much o' a summer either."

I looked away. Who was Jimmy? Why

was he addressing my husband as Jimmy? Why did he use words that I had to strain to understand?

No, not the BBC English of received pronunciations that I had heard on the radio in Madras, or in the manner of speech from the nuns who had taught me at school. *I need to attune myself to a new kind of language* I told myself.

Our one-bedroom flat on Kelvin Drive was in a huge blonde sandstone house, opposite the Botanic Gardens in the West End of Glasgow. The landlady was charming and pointed out how lucky we were to stay near the University and Byres Road with its almost bohemian mixture of students. The BBC was just on Queen Margaret Drive too, she added.

I settled in slowly. The acclimatization took a while, to the language, the weather, and a new life living in one room compared to the huge house, gardens and constant stream of friends and family.

The silence was strange, almost sepulchral while my husband as at work all day. Mrs Reid, the landlady, had pointed out Hillhead library to me and I registered, was given a yellow paper library ticket. That piece of card was my comfort in those days; as was the discovery of the Victorian Kibble Palace, the tropical house with its banana plants reaching to its glass ceilings, the crotons, familiar herbs, the huge palms which made me feel at home.

The warmth and light inside the place made me think of Madras. It was the daily walk to Byres Road to buy my newspaper *The Glasgow Herald*, through the Botanic Gardens that made me take some interest in the trees and bushes that were on my path.

It was autumn and the purple rhododendrons were in full bloom. I had not seen such a profusion of these plants in Madras. I asked Mrs Reid and she described them as plants from the Himalayas, brought over by Scottish botanists during the early 18th Century.

I was fascinated and ashamed I knew so little of my new country's landscape and its flora and fauna. So, I got a book out of the library to look up some of the common ones I came across in Glasgow. The heathers were immediately recognizable. The roses in some of the gardens were a joy to behold. Bunches of the floribunda's variety, the climbing roses and the miniature ones were a treat to the eyes, even if few had the heady scent of the Indian rose, the Gulab.

The tiny rosehip bulbs on the bushes were new to me, as were the beautiful red berries of the Rowan tree. I had missed the beauty of the cherry blossom that lasted only a few weeks in June or July.

The landscape was golden. The leaves shaken off the trees by the chilling winds were carpeting the pavements in various shades of gold and browns. Sepia tones in some of them, blood-red in some others. The colours were stunning like nature weaving a carpet on the soggy ground. I remembered one of the school homework tasks of collecting leaves and drying them in the pages of a book. The dried leaves became skeletal and yet the imprint seemed like veins on our hands. The leaves I discovered could also be slippery and I did miss my footing once. The danger in beauty especially when you don't wear the right footwear was evident.

One scene inspired me to write a short poem. A lone bright red leaf lay among a pile of brown leaves in the Botanic Gardens.

Vermillion

Leaves fall, blown away in the autumnal blitz

Gold strewn paths crunch and crackle underfoot

A single vermillion leaf like a teardrop stands
proud

Defiant, blood red, life courses through its
veins.

The widow looks askance; the blood-red leaf
sends a shiver

The memory of her wedding day, a bride
adorned with jewels

The red sindoor in the parting of her hair,
beginning a new life

Of wedded love, happiness, babies, the start of
a journey.

The sudden death of her spouse, the ritual of
her widowhood

An awakening of the day as the sindoor on her
forehead is wiped away

The bindi, the dot, the point at which creation
begins, negated forever

The jangle of broken glass as bangles are
crushed and ornaments discarded.

The white sari envelopes her shroud-like, a
colourless palette

Life of the walking dead bereft of feelings, love
or emotion.

Vermillion turned to ash, grey, unassuming as
the leaden skies.

The blood-red leaf is trodden under the
walker's brisk steps.

***

Women in India had to give up all
ornaments or decoration including the
simple red dot on their forehead; it
was like their lives stopped when their
husbands died. It is no longer followed
in the cities but the ritual wiping away of
the *'sindoor'* is still a tradition that is done

during the mourning period of a widow in the Hindu religion.

Autumn drew to a close with Hallowe'en celebrated in all the shops with the pumpkin making its appearance in some shop windows. Being a vegetarian and having tasty meals prepared for me at home, shopping for groceries was an eye-opener for me. Apart from carrots, turnip, potatoes, leeks there were few greens at all. I had to do with tinned peas and beans; the variety of vegetables that I had taken for granted in Madras was a rarity here.

I realized slowly that the many aspects of my life were changing irrevocably but there were so many other experiences that were enriching.

I had never witnessed seasons changing in Madras. It was either hot, hotter or the short spell of the monsoons that were a relief from the heat. The months of November and December had a slight reduction in the temperatures but not significantly different.

Autumn changing to winter was beguiling. The odd days when we had sunshine, rain, a bit of frost and warmth, all four seasons in a day, was a new experience.

Margareth Stewart

Margareth Stewart is the pen name of published Italian writer Monica Mastrantonio. She holds a PhD in Social Psychology and is a visiting professor at the University of York. Her stories: *Open - Pierre's journey after WW2* and *Mademoiselle-sur-Seine* are available to purchase online. Margareth spends every moment she can in the Scottish town of Montrose where she has her writer's base. She is currently working on a feminist thriller called *Zero Chance*. She is a mum to three and she loves all things literature.

Montrose

Montrose is a place
where the sky shines
with grace
Montrose is a place
where everyone lives
and does not race
Montrose is a place
where young people
play as mates
Montrose is a place
where fair trade is
a must and a scale

Montrose is a place
where sea is grey in unsettled waves
Montrose is a place
where wind blows in grades
Montrose is a place
where my heart bows with laces

Montrose is a place
where passion has its own pace
Montrose is a place
where no matter the path or
the trace

Neither the matters nor the dates
If you're tall, short or aged
Solid is Scotland
in the palms of the greatest

Brave is Scotland
in the height of my embrace
High is Scotland

Together with my mates

Thanks for everything!

When the Sky is

When the sky is blue and lilac
When the sky is blue and pink

When the sky is pink and orange
When the sky is black and grey
When the sky is blue and navy
When the sky is orange and blue
When the sky is grey and blue
When the sky is dark blue
Who is painting it?
Who is painting it?
Who is painting it?

In Scotland?
Shhhhhh. The giants.

In Ferryden

In Ferryden, I've drunk,
Far too much
Far too often
In Ferryden

        In Ferryden, I've gambled,
           Far too much
           Far too often
           In Ferryden

In Ferryden, I've sailed,
Far too much
Far too often
In Ferryden

        In Ferryden, I've seen,
           Far too much
           Far too often
           In Ferryden

In Ferryden, I've loved
Just once
In Ferryden.

Melanie L. Wells-Alvarado

Melanie is a writer, artist, photographer, and sailor who lives in Costa Rica. She writes children's stories, adventures, adult fiction, and inspirational tales. She has produced a photo documentary about the indigenous people in the jungles of Costa Rica.

In 2017 and 2018, she received two consecutive grants from the US Embassy in Costa Rica to set up photo exhibits in the capital, and to create a travelling exhibition.

In early 2021, her photo exhibition, *A Window into the Soul* opened to the public at the Jade Museum in San José, Costa Rica.

www.melwellsphotography.com

Salty air, quiet cove

My skin trembles with the kiss of the salty air, the hazy sky before me, grey silhouettes in the distance. I can almost touch the isles, yet the wind keeps forcing us to tack in zigzag, we are almost there, yet, we keep on sailing in place.

His short grey hair flies in the wind, his arms around me solid as the roots of a 100-year-old tree, his scent mingles with the ocean air. I inhale him, I inhale life. I am warm. I can sail like this forever. His dark piercing eyes smile at me. I shiver as his hand like fine sandpaper touches my cheek, his lips though, are soft and silky.

Time must have frozen, when I look up, the entrance of Acarsaid Mhor is in front of us. The craggy mountains on both sides remind me of him, of sailing into Bermuda, but no, this is Scotland, my Scotland. For a split second, I am transported hundreds of years back, when the simple act of everyday life was pure survival.

This weekend is to be ours, camping on the boat, away from everyone, just the two of us. We'll do survival our style, with a soft feather duvet and dry smooth red wine.

The sails luff a bit as we enter the pass, land is very close on our port side, my stomach tightens, I hold the anchor line ready to drop.

"Almost there, lass" his wide smile shines his face, his gentle gestures caress my heart. I stare at him, we both sowed our wild oats in our youth. Now in our 50's we are confident and peaceful. Had we met years ago, would we had made it this far? Now, we fit like a glove.

"Aye, I'll be at the helm at departure", I wink at him.

"Whatever you desire lass".

Beep, beep, beep, beep…

"That's odd. I'll check the depth sounder, but we should be in deep enough waters" he mumbles.

Beep, beep, beep, beep… I open my eyes startled. "Ughh…What…Oh no…"

As I reach for my phone to stop the alarm, the smooth papers with the KLM logo fall to the ground.

"Soon, my dear Scotland, soon."

BLUE ACHE

Áine King

Áine is a playwright, storyteller and
artist. An Irish East-Ender, she studied
at Brighton and Sussex and at R.A.D.A.
Áine's screenplay, *Running Out*, about
life during lockdown, was filmed for the
National Theatre Scotland/BBC Scotland's
Scenes For Survival in 2020. She is currently
writing a play about invisible disability
for the Birds Of Paradise Theatre Co. Áine
lives in the Orkney Islands.

www.aineking.net

Sea Creatures

I look human.
I can *pass* for human. On a good day.
Sitting in the front seat
In the minibus.
Until folks see the Blue Badge and
the wheelchair lift.
Then their gaze turns and ebbs away.
I'm in the wrong skin.
Entangled in my own wreckage,
And out of my depth.

Tuesdays and Fridays,
We drive along the sea road
To the new swimming pool.
The ocean winks in sunshine,
Or hauls itself overboard in a grey-green
gale.
Just an inch of open window is allowed,
Where I gulp and tilt my nose into the
tang of brine.

We park in our own bay
At the pool.
Here, in this concrete bunker,
Water is penned and pissed in.
I'm stripped and wrapped and hoisted
like cargo,
Swung out over the shallows and lowered
into Ossian's hold.
Pierced and braided and tattooed
He stands
Thigh-deep,
A mythical warrior, freshly-leapt from
a longboat.

He steers me,
Steady,
Fingers skimming my silver-grey one-piece
Expertly pretending not to feel the narrow
bag of shit
Taped to my hip.
He tugs and tows me
into deep water,

Laughing like a pirate.

You're a selkie seal-woman
He grins,
Braids and tattoos dripping.
I imagine touching my tongue to those
rivulets
Tasting not him, but the liquid light of
streaming water
Searching for some trace of his strength in it,
A homeopathy of his Health
As if I could sip
Him
And heal.
You're a little mermaid he says
Flexing my flipper-feet
Spreading my toes with his big brown
fingers.
My lips part,
Unseen,
Wet and plump as sea anemones.

Mermaids weep to walk,
Their perfect pretty feet
Shredded and splintered at every step.
You can keep dry land
And the dull choke of earth.
I'll dance on the ocean floor
And sleep on the seabed,
Treasured.

I want the fierce, fickle hug of the tide.
Let it come in and fill me
Drenched
Head and groin
With walloping waves
Slapping my chest,
Closing my eyes
With Salt-Stinging kisses.

I am flotsam, wreckage
Drifting towards a beach somewhere,
Treacherous as undertow.
Dancing underwater, seal-circling my prey

Close as I dare
Stirring the fur on his chest like fronds

Winding him in the weeds of my hair
Flashing between his thighs
Flickering over his lips
Stealing his breath.

Ossian's gaze, a grey splash
As he watches the clock
Above a sea-stack
Of plastic floats on the poolside
And wishes himself ashore.

I am a selkie
Sleek
And hard to hold.
Every breath heaves
Every step
Bleeds.
One day soon I will slip away
Slip

The brake
On the chair or the bus
Slip down the slip
Slip out of my skin and into the water
And go hunting
For sailors
To kiss.

Isobel Stewart

Isobel was born in Scotland and inherited her parents love of travel.

During her literary career, she has produced short stories for women's magazines, articles for Scottish magazines and stories for children. She is also the creator and author of *Pod Inter Galactic Traveller*. She blogs about places she has travelled to and has just finished her first novel. Her new book is called *Legends of the Ancients: From the Mists of Time*.

www.podigt.co.uk

The Foreboding Valley of Glencoe

*H*aunting. Atmospheric. Melancholy. This is the Valley of Glencoe.

As a child, I would travel north with my parents every year, to the town of Oban, for our summer holidays. Instead of taking the route over the Connel Bridge, we would take the longer road snaking through the majestic beauty to be found in the mountains and moors of the Valley of Glencoe.

This dramatic landscape made such an impression upon me that there was no question as to where my husband and I should take our honeymoon. That meant we spent an amazing autumnal week staying in the historic Kingshouse Hotel, from which we could view the foreboding mountain of Buachaille Etive Mòr.

Fifty years later and many visits in-between, we once again found ourselves in the shadow of that spectacular, snow-capped mountain.

I often contemplate what it is that makes people return to Glencoe on a regular basis. Perhaps it is the history of an atrocious slaughter that took place in the valley on February 13th, 1692 when 30 members of the clan MacDonald were brutally slaughtered by Robert Campbell, Commander of the Earl of Argyll's regiment, for not accepting allegiance to King William III of Scotland. An impression of doom and gloom invades the valley in that area and ghosts of the Clan MacDonald are said to roam the heather-covered hills seeking revenge against the Campbells. Easy to imagine as it feels as if one has stepped back in history to the days of Rob Roy or

Bonnie Prince Charlie rushing down the mountains, shield and sword in hand.

Then again, perhaps it is the natural beauty of the landscape that captures delight within one's soul. Leaving the stark and barren Loch Rannoch Moor behind, one enters the valley by crossing a picturesque bridge over the turbulent waters of the River Coe. Venturing off the road overlooked by brooding mountains on either side, one is transported into a magical world of hidden rivers, spectacular waterfalls, and unseen valleys. Due to the harsh cold, wet landscape, wildlife is limited but red deer, roe deer and the shy fox might be seen.

The valley is also famous for a variety of adventure sports. Sports such as climbing, walking, skiing and snowboarding, paragliding and mountain biking. In winter, the ski-lift takes enthusiastic skiers high up into the snow-covered mountains.

One might be lucky on a trip to the top to encounter a spectacular golden eagle in flight.

Ask me what is the 'real' Scotland, I would have no hesitation in saying, the Valley of Glencoe; its magical spell mesmerises all.

Mina Millar

Mina Millar writes Mystery Suspense novels and poetry. She also specialises in novellas – perfect for the impatient modern mind – and is currently working on a sixth Mina Millar Romantic Suspense novella called *The Wrong Man*. She divides her time between London, Scotland and Europe.

Lockdown Days
February 2021

The greyest of lockdown days
We're reaching for the rope and
we go our separate ways.

Me, with thoughts of naked
bodies, just to feel, anything to feel.
I hate being mean.
You brooding in a red hot stew.
Flashing lights from neon screens.

With a foot on the pedal I am there in
Blairadam
Silence except for the roar of the M90
saddle.
Silence except for the cry in my heart
Silence and then silence and then I am in
it and my mind is stark.

Those words, something silly, a voice
from the green
Skeletal fingers reaching up to the sky
invisibly scream.

Gun-coloured
Coal stones
Glitter grey
Prickly green, the scent of Christmas trees
and buckets of play.

Old men in battle watching over the little
babies
The walk-walk-walk over mud and the
plenty of maybes.

The sing-sing-sing within
The bliss-bliss-bliss of the encircling.

And then there was nobody
Because nobody came
The thick heavy sky turns bruised-black
And I am gone
Back.

Journey

Who comes like this?
Dropped from the sky into my world.
When does this ever happen?
Never.

But for once and then the date. Never.
When it can never be. Simple.
When it cannot be allowed to be.
There is a slice of pleasure. Gifted.
A moment in time. Packaged.
A softness in the autumn light. Chilled.

Steps on glistening stones, over to the
sands of St.Andrews. Lightly.
And then sunken under grey skies. The
taste of you. Spritely.
The half-hour to the full-hour, the dropping
in, the stones, the sand and then your
mouth. On mine. And your body in mine.

Forced.
But wanted.
Who are you?
What am I?

BRIGHT MIST

Ann MacKinnon

Ann MacKinnon writes poetry in both Scots and English, and has been published in various anthologies and magazines.

She has had four poetry pamphlets published, the latest being *Nae Wirds* by Tapsalteerie Press.

In 2018 she was shortlisted for her poem *Central Station* in the Wigtown Poetry Prize in Wigtown, Scotland's National Book Town, and in 2019 she was a joint-winner in the McCash Poetry Competition for her poem *Climmin Ben Lomond*.

The Surge of the Sea

Her body is a cello,
clothed in yellow flowers.
She rises from the sea
pouring out her music,
praising the Gaelic.
Her red hair is plaited in
a double helix - proof
of her birth right.

Around her fishermen
cast their nets on the waves
as the sea surges.
The ocean is roaring,
sweeping the sand.
The eternal tide
of her culture is sewn
in every thread.
Above, wild geese fly,
following their leader,

forming and reforming,
just like the tide, flowing
in its circular journey,
calling to her to soar
and sing her song,
the Surge of the Sea.

Inspired by Panel 159 of *The Great Tapestry of Scotland*. Alistair Moffat (Author), Susan Mansfield (Author). Foreword by Alexander McCall Smith. Published by Birlinn Ltd.

Manvinder Reid

A Scottish writer, born in Glasgow, Manvinder has a diverse background which fuels her writing. She has written stories for children, has published several online non-fiction articles and is working on her first novel. A mum-of-two living in Glasgow, Manvinder is a member of the Bearsden Writers Group.

www.bearsdenwriters.org

Deceive Me While I Admire You

They say you are beautiful but
they don't know what I know.

They say you are beautiful but
they don't feel lashings
on tear-struck cheeks, or how
you whip me with my own wet hair.

They say you are beautiful, but don't
see how you deceive,
how you lure me into an idyll
which upon entrance becomes
a deathly cliff 'pon which I teeter.
How beautiful can you be, when
you laugh and say 'come',
your wide-open arms giving way to rocks
which bring me crashing to my knees.

Why do you beckon with
sunshine on your head, before

emptying all the rain in the sky
on weary me?
The sight of you afar makes me tingle
and itch to be near you.
Reds, greens, orange and brown
mesmerise me.

Once in your lair, all colours become quiet
so very quiet
shh.
You throw a blanket of
grey, black and grey
a sweeping cape to cover me.
Don't let me see through the grey,
or hear through the wind,
feel through the cold or
taste any but my tears.

I hear you laugh, wicked and loud
'I am beautiful though' bellowing proud
Beautiful they say, when you invite us
to share your form, so welcome.

How cruel you are then, when solitude sets.

They say you are beautiful, and I say it too.
I say you are beautiful, my sweet, I do.

THE LONGING

Farah Haq

Farah is a born and bred Glaswegian. She fell in love with writing at a young age and never recovered.

Today she is pursuing her dream of being published, in between the demands of her career as a Process Engineer and being a mum to two wee boys.

Her inspiration for this piece lies in her experiences of growing up in the West End; the sights, sounds and smells that embody that lively and vibrant part of the city. It's an ode to her parents, whose love and never-failing support drive who she is and everything she does.

She currently lives in Berkshire with her husband and young sons but returns to visit her hometown regularly.

My heart and my home

*T*he cold wet air grabs and envelopes me like only a Glasgow spring can.
Within seconds my face is sodden, the cold wetness dripping down my face.

A sudden intake of air and I'm left breathless. Yet there is a familiarity and a beautiful warmth about it.

As I step out onto the bustling street I'm greeted by all the familiar sights and sounds. Traffic is stretching from one horizon to the other and horns are singing their melodious tunes.

Children stand drenched, huddled in groups, head jolted back, laughing, as their mouths sing clouds of vapour. The waft of the chippie fills my nose and I'm transported back to a time when homework and growing pains were the main stay of life.

As I wander down the road I'm greeted by grinning faces and nods of the head, and as I reciprocate, my heart skips a beat. I realise there is just no place like this.

I'm home again.

Gayle Smith

Gayle Smith is a transwoman and spoken-word poet from Baillieston. She co-hosts the long-running *Words And Music* night, at the Milk Cafe on Victoria Road, Glasgow, with her friend Jen Hughes. She has performed her work throughout Scotland since 1993 and is particularly proud of her connection with the *Other Voices* and *Women With Fierce Words* spoken-word collectives.

Her work has been published in a number of publications both in print and online including *The Best of 10red* Edited By (Kevin Cadwallender), *Women With Fierce Words* An Anthology (Edited By Lesley Traynor), *Mind The Time* (An Anthology of Football Memories Edited By Jim MacKintosh).

The Crossing

In the bracing late winter air
I stood at the top of goatfell
discovering myself
in moments alone with nature

I knew, just as dusk began to set
on Arran skies
I could no longer lie
to myself or anyone else
a journey had to start

My heart screamed woman
calling me, by a name
not yet chosen
telling me she will take me home
but to ready myself
and prepare for the crossing

There would be significant storms

before arriving
on the shores, of a place
where I would finally be myself
having completed the route
she mapped in a geographers heart

As I stood at the top of the island
I breathed in the force of her power
allowing her to take me where she must
to learn what I needed to know
to blossom into the full bloom of my truth

The Haunting

Haunted
ghosts from her past
attempt to steal her future

they claim to see to see visions
place limits on where she is allowed to go

in the darkness
they visit her
using it's blanket
to disguise their true intentions

on the day she awakens
at the dawn of first light
she will claim her independence

On this morning no matter the season
she will find her chosen path

her predator diminished by her laughter
will need to find new prey

The radiance of daylight shows a woman
discarding the rags she once wore
no longer will she
be visited by ghosts
as their boasts and screams fade away
she accepts the power of day

and as she views the sunrise
she will never again
know the haunting

Chris Tait

Chris Tait is a poet, fantasy writer, playwright and spoken-word artist. She attends writer's groups and open mic sessions, reads on the radio, at gigs and festivals across Scotland and has recorded poetry in a studio.

She has published two graphic novels, has had writing commissioned and published in books and websites. She writes in English and Shetland dialect.

She has had plays and monologues performed by actors as well.

Instagram @taitchris6

A Viking's dream

Row, row, row your boat
Gently down the stream
Over to Shetland's moat
In a Viking's dream

Stones skim past childhood
Through a star sequence
Clearances did intrude
Sheep were a sad audience

Miles of green thickets
Sewn from Norse god's tools
Aquarius' bucket
Excalibur in rock pools

Villages like horse shoes
Hills with crowns of thorns
Amulets are ploughs
Birds respond to horns

At the last supper
Winds did huff and puff
With the laird's scuppers
The folk sailed from cuffs

A ship like a feather
Over a rinsed dram
People on a short tether
Loaned from a ram

RECAPTURE

Bidisha Chakraborty

Bidisha Chakraborty, a postgraduate student in English Language and Literature from University of Calcutta, currently working as an Academic Research Writer, teacher and a poet. She lives and breathes Scotland and longs to visit it again someday.

My Dream is Scotland

*I*have reached my dream destination, Scotland, a place I have dreamt about so often. This country, wrapped within nature's captivating beauty with stunning mountains, highlands, yards, giant arches, waterfalls and islands, is the land of my childhood and my adolescence. But only in my inner world. In India, I saw in the books of my studies and the literature I loved, the rhythm and flow of this magical place.

And now I am here, in this panoramic land with its most pleasant of climates, neither scorching hot, yet sometimes freezing cold. I love the visual feasts for my eyes, with memories that stored within the gallery of mind, a thing for eternity.

Scotland's secrets are the surprising views that one receives from the high rugged mountains, highlands, bridges and castles. And in the flesh, in reality, these sights are more reassuring and beautiful than anything on the page of a book.

Grasslands are surrounded with mountains all around and they are the guardians of the natural environment from ages back.

I am going to the Cairngorms in the manner of Nan Shepherd to wallow in the sensuality of her words. The Cairngorms are a range of misty mountains of the Eastern Highlands where one can discover the highest summits of UK.

I often think about this hard yet beautiful land and how its geography and culture has made this proud and firm people. The Scots have been living within this natural environment for so long that their nature and traditions have been influenced with natural traits.

The authenticity and sweetness of the

Gaelic language describes Scotland's unique position from the rest of the English and Welsh landmass and is so lovely.

Generosity and humbleness seem to define the Scottish landscape. The Fairy Glen defines the purity and evergreen beauty of this natural habitat along with a famous myth that fairies and angels visit it.

The recurring beauty of Scotland is a living element, as if the mountains were one's companion and the rocks - witness to the changes that took place on Earth over millions of years ago – are your friend.

I listen. I am still. I hear the sounds of the falling water, winds flirting with the murmuring leaves. I see the brightness of the flowers; types I recognize from my home in India. Nature has a language all of its own. It's poetry, music, painting, art. Nature is everything.

In Scotland, nature becomes history, philosophy and science. It's a beautiful thing, a thing for all of us, from wherever we hail. And to Scotland, I am so grateful, for everything she gives.

Nyala

Nyala is an Eritrean refugee into Scotland.
She lives in Aberdeen and is a passionate
cook and poet. She writes regularly and
constructs poetry in her mind, while
she prepares her dishes for her catering
business. She is currently learning English
and is hoping to be fully fluent as soon
as possible. Her love of Scotland is fast
overtaking her love of her homeland, and
for that she is grateful.

Stone-cold life

Whispers of ultimate
freedom
From a stone-cold cage
The silence is screaming
For eternity
But only for a moment in time

Show the way
Long lost days
Colour on burning cold grey

New light – begging old
Stone forgotten pathways

Flash of hope – long lost dreams

Sunlight dances like a
Spirit of lost souls
Grinding life through

Cold stone pathways
To nowhere
Open doors to everywhere

Momentarily blinded by
light
To see
The darkness beyond.

Mary Monro

Mary is a Registered Osteopath living in Edinburgh, treating people and animals. Her first book was *Stranger In My Heart* (Unbound, 2018), a memoir of her father's WWII heroics and her quest to explore his life. It received coverage in the UK national press, various magazines and the South China Morning Post. She spoke about it at the Bristol Literature Festival and Shrewsbury Literature Festival in 2018.

Mary's great-aunt, Dora Metcalf, who lived at Swordlands in the Scottish Highlands, is the subject of her work-in-progress, *Power On*, a novel based on Dora's life as a tech entrepreneur and founder of the information services industry.

www.dorapower.co.uk

To Swordlands

Swordlands – the name of this house has been rumbling around my mind like distant thunder. Heavy, potent, it seems to come from the age of chivalry and bloody death. It glints, piercing the present from the dark past, evoking images of candlelit men, battle-weary and sodden from the hammering rain, roaring fires and roasting fowl.

The name belongs to a Victorian hunting lodge in the Scottish Highlands, on the shore of Loch Morar, the former home of my great-aunt Dora. Swordlands is a house of secrets. It was a training centre for spies in the Second World War, but there is no trace of exactly what happened there. During the war, my great-aunt's company made the *'bombe machines'* used by Alan Turing to break the secret Enigma code. Are these facts somehow connected? They have the feel of a forest whose connecting filaments are deeply hidden, but I can only see the separate trees, not quite touching. My great-aunt chose to retire to this most remote house in her seventies, an unsuitable choice by most people's standards. *What did she know?*

I drive to the Highlands in November. Lashing rain, short, dark days, gusts threatening to shove me into the path of oncoming trucks.

I want to walk along the track towards the house anyway. The last leaves cling to the trees, hiding their modesty from the bodice-ripping wind. Intensely green, velvety moss, crimson berries and coppery broken-stemmed bracken splash colour across the grey-brown water, rock and skyscape. It's six miles to Swordlands and I know I won't make it.

The first mile or two hint at the length and depth of the narrow loch, with the hillside rearing above, daring me to continue. There's a ruined chapel on the shore, its sacred space spilled and scattered by the greater power of nature.

The path is treacherous. At times an ill-fitting rocky jigsaw, then teasing bog, pretending solidity but letting out gurgled laughter as stinking mud oozes over the cuff of my boot. I'll try again in the summer.

A crystal-clear September day. Lapis sky, mirrored loch, but I'm nervous. It's a tough hike and there's no choice.

Covid means there's no ferry, no boats for hire. My local guide is older than me but mountain-fit. He thinks we should continue past Swordlands to visit Tarbet with its croft and chapel.

I think twelve miles of rough terrain
is enough for my bunioned feet and
arthritic knees and then rebuke myself
for my feebleness. My great-aunt and
her husband lived in this house in their
seventies, when there was no electricity,
water came from the burn and a boat was
the only way to get the groceries, weather
permitting.

I hope to glimpse the house as an
encouragement that we are nearing our
goal, but it guards its privacy with a
cloak of rowan, oak and birch, with firs to
ensure year-round protection.

Even on a perfect day the track is tricky,
with slippery slabs of rock, steep climbs
and tumbling burns to cross. My guide
says *not much further* and *we're almost there*
according to his GPS. A lizard basks on a
glittering rock, eyes us and darts away. A
lizard! Is he a sentinel? A raven *"craaks"*

overhead, wheeling in the unboundaried
blue. Is she signalling our arrival?

At last we see Swordlands below us,
a three-gabled fortress alone on a bank.
Below it at the shore is a boathouse, a
cottage and a jetty jutting out into the flat
calm water.

I walk round the house, peering in. The
Factor has given us permission, but the
house rescinds it. I sit on the verandah and
am still, softly gazing across the loch to
the hills beyond. I wait with all my senses
alert and open, ready to receive, but this
house of spies gives only the feeling that it
is actively blocking communication.

I wonder if my great-aunt treasured this
integrity, felt that the burden of her own
secrets was shared by Swordlands. A safe
haven, an unbreachable boundary for a
life spent holding her tongue. I smile and
let go.

SKIN-TO-SKIN

Finola Scott

Glaswegian Finola Scott's poems are on posters, tapestries and postcards. They are published widely in the UK & the Republic of Ireland, including *New Writing Scotland, Ink Sweat & Tears, Orbis* and *Lighthouse*. Red Squirrel Press published her pamphlet *Much Left Unsaid*. More of her poems can be found on Facebook at Finola Scott Poems.

Walking through time
(Lenzie Moss, Glasgow)

Streams gurgle as I follow the
track edging the ancient muir.

Reaching the grassland I feel the
opening, the emptying, the blue.

My lungs sing, each breath a cool drink.
My senses zing.

Cloudless, the sky is wide, vast.
I turn, turn my head to try to catch and
hold it all.
Grasses gleam.
The press of tree-tops ends and silence
slips in.

Here peat is metres deep, here centuries of
silken leaves turned to mulch then pressed
to peat.

Dark below and so bright above.
Here light is Queen. She glints on the
softly shifting surface of standing pools,
bestows grace on her cotton grasses.

Underfoot all is spongy, rich brown,
unsolid, strangely unsettling. I feel my
muscles stretch and tighten, become
aware of pressure on pads of feet, the
weight of bones.

So near home yet it's an adventure. I sense
but do not see the scuffling, scamperings
of foxes rabbits, voles, mice.

They are all autumn hungry. Only tiny
sounds as long grass sways gives them
away. Now boardwalks tempt me to
meander the mire. They steady my
progress, the patter of my feet reassures.

Beside me metal-held canals and dams

struggle to master brackish water. I savour the wet woody air.

A line of silver is a heron hunched ever patient. I stop, breathe and watch, try to absorb the solitude. I feel my pores open, oxygen surges my veins. I am alive, in this moment.

Now. I remember to wait, to look at the small, to seek the infinitesimal. No silver wings of damselflies flutter grasses or foxgloves today.

The season has turned. As early sun winter-sets, slicing low, birches barks glow molten. Gilded, the landscape is hushed. I feel myself still, heart slow.

Senses alert, brain stops processing information, the history of the peat can wait. Now I reach to touch rough bark,

moss carpeted. Boots slide on silken
leaves. There is no external, no cars, trains,
only here, this wood, the sound and feel of
soft sphagnum's squelch.

Humanity is me alone here, breathing.

Above raucous crows begin to call and
gather. Their torn shapes tangle branches.
Topmost boughs sough as long-tailed
tits alight to final-forage. Twittering they
cement relationships.

Bees and swallows are long gone. In
thickening dusk, ghostly hawk moths take
their turns, begin to hunt.

Soothed by it all, I head home.

Fiona H. Preston

Fiona lives in South Lanarkshire in Scotland, and has been spending holidays in Mallaig for around 25 years.

Her trilogy, *The Arnasaid Series* was set in the area between Mallaig and Arisaig, Inverness-shire.

The first two books are available online from bookshops and Amazon worldwide. She is now a full-time writer and has written many children's books too, not yet published.

She is interested in music, is part of a large choir in Glasgow called 'Merchant Voices', and loves walking in the countryside with her two small dogs.

My Aching Heart

Scotland is a land of contrasts. There is an abundance of pretty fishing villages from Eyemouth to St. Andrews and Crail in the East, to Port Patrick, Ayr, the Argyle coast and up to Ullapool on the West.

The Central Belt lies like a sleeping industrial giant torn between East and West, claiming some accolade with scenic hills, the Mendips and Campsies, the austere Ben Lomond rising like a Jacobite past the self-consciousness of the lower land.

Then there are inland delights; the rolling hills of Perthshire and the borders radiating calm, and the spectacular mountain regions of Grampians, with Ben Nevis and the Cairngorms fueling my sense with adventure.

My heart aches for the North West,
where my writing is born and dies; where
my creative juices flow, like the gentle
gurgling of the Highland streams. My
destiny is carved in the rocky mountain
pathways.

Words pour like the tumultuous
seas and lie sparking like the stealthy
waterways creeping through the
Caledonian Canal.

On the journey of some hundred miles
from home to Mallaig, I see the differing
landscapes of what seems like several
countries rolled into one. The mountains
are my travel partners for most of the
journey, the lochs and glens age-old
escape routes. The smell of the sea invades
my nostrils, making me crave a fresh
fish supper. The Isle of Skye bobs on the
waves, its frothing water can be seen in the
distance, crashing onto its shores.

The first time I saw Mallaig, I felt

that some ethereal force had pulled me to the town. Nestled in the shadow of the Grampian peaks and the ranges of Knoydart and Skye, ideas for stories trip through my mind as quickly as the burns career down the hills into the lochs.

I slake my thirst on the revitalising atmosphere as I drive into the town and out past the dancing waters of the harbour to the holiday house. Eating and drinking in this place feels almost spiritual. The food and wine my communion, the mountain tops, my altar.

The land is a husband, sedentary and solid. The mountains are friends, stentorian in their advice and imposing natural beauty. The sea a lover constantly changing, dangerous; wild one minute then calm and ingratiating, lapping frothily to shore, tickling my toes and sending a charge through my body making me want to walk on water, renouncing convention and beliefs.

On a walk around Loch Morar from the shores of Loch Nevis I am the last person on earth. The deepest loch in Britain ringed by mountains surveying my every tread. Morag, the mystical monster doesn't surface, but I can feel her presence.

The soft ripples of the water tell of lurking beneath, but the loch radiates a friendliness, an insecurity and a forsaken destiny, which I am sure no one else must understand but me.

The many white sandy beaches feel all comfortingly sublime. A shifting platform of peace on my tired feet. The seas a healing green, not the expected blue or black starkness. The skies ever-changing, devilish clouds vie with heavenly shades of red and purple, producing breath-taking sunsets. Here the world opens up, the colours change with the hour, as often does the weather. There is no sense of time, the land goes on to the end of the earth and to a life beyond.

Back at the cottage, I am enthused and feel complete. A roaring fire the background, with the sounds around me, the foghorn, the wind hurtles through the glen; I shiver, but I am not alone. The house falls open to the world, has no walls. I am inexplicably conjoined with nature.

My existence and true meaning live in this place, I escape within. It consumes me, wraps around me, I ponder my own mortality. This land has been here for millions of years. We are here but a short time then we return to the land, replenish the soil and are born again in the elements. I try to write my journal. I know not where to begin, all I know is that this place nurtures and fulfils me and will lead me to words.

Jen Hughes

Jen Hughes is a writer from Ayrshire, and an English Literature and Film & TV Studies student at University of Glasgow. She has been passionate about writing since she could hold a pencil. She has been performing her work regularly for years, and has been co-hosting the Open Mic night, *Words and Music*, with Gayle Smith since 2018. Her debut chapbook, *Keep On Spinning* has been published by Dreich Publishing is available now from their online store and from Jen's website. If you enjoy her work, you can find more on her website jenhugheswriter.com.

Ease Deeper

Beautiful feeling, beautiful
meeting
I want to melt into your arms
more
Than anything
But I don't trust things that are pleasing.
This pleasure could be deceiving.
My soul glows for you in my eyes.
I can't blink, I can't hide
What I feel inside.

You're a hot bath after a stressful day.
You're the warmth that dissolves my woes
Like the scented salt and suds in the
waters below.
I want you close, always.
I should say,

You're '*Ibuleve*' for my tenseness.
I don't know if I'm senseless

From the cold showers I've lived with.
So long, the lukewarm denying my senses
My limbs are tingling, pins and needles
but nice
I must say it tonight.

I've never been great at being concise,
Using five verses when three words
suffice:
I feel safe
I feel loved
I'm not wrong
I can relax
You are right

I want to ease deeper with you.
I want to spend my life with you
I love you.

Sadie Maskery

Sadie Maskery lives in Scotland by the sea with her family. She was a jazz singer until lockdown. Her writing will be found in various publications both online and in print, and she is on Twitter as @saccharinequeen where she describes herself, optimistically, as "functioning adequately."

TANTALLON

I love Tantallon.
I hate Tantallon.
There is too much time saturating
its bones, and the bones go too deep.
The castle is a magnificently
destroyed crown, jewels all ripped away.
It balances at the edge of cliffs, above a
sea that shifts from periwinkle to deepest
black, fields sweeping like robes behind
and so much blood shed defending the
glory of its lairds that the memory of it
seeps from the sandstone with the dew.

On a bleak day you feel the wind cut
slices from your cheeks. You gaze through
the shattered keep across the Forth to Bass
Rock.

You bear it for a while, the dankness of
the stone, the pain of the cold. Then you
retreat to huddle in a corner in sympathy

with some 15th century soldier who
found the same nook and cursed the same
savage rain slapping across eyes and
insinuating between hood and nape.

In the summer, seabirds cast shadows
on the parapets and you can drape your
body along green mounds delineating
long dismantled walls, the smell of new
cut grass melding with the sweet salt tang
of the sea.

Soft Scottish sunshine seems to swaddle
you, bees hum a lament to the slain and
you drowse to dream of iron clashing on
stone, fire, and always and ever the wind
prising at invisible cracks in life's facade.

But time - the reality of time - terrifies
you here if you let your mind slip beyond
the neat bounds of known history. The
layers are dense beyond imagination,
humanity a mere scum on the surface.
Signs point out the scenes of great deeds
(and the souvenir shop).

Helpful guides in gilets will tell you of
trebuchets, cannons, heros and murderers.
And yes, we died here. Ghosts linger.
There was fear and betrayal and battles
and all that meandered in between, the
loving and birthing, all the music, shit and
despair; laughter, a little.

Small lives and deaths that happened
quietly - the passage of unimportant
people while kings and earls imposed
themselves on the pages of history, not
noticing that the margins were crumbling
even as it was written.

The ghosts are fading too, clockwork
toys winding down, skirling softly in
draughty tunnels, shimmering whirls
of past drama in helpless replay, a
chronological echo of sorts. They waft
across the souls of a sensitive visitor,
shadows tugging at stray threads
of unease. But young, they are so
young, mere centuries, still raw with

bewilderment at their passing even as they dissolve into dreams.

The battlements they haunt are made of the bones of the truly ancient dead. The world belonged to them completely too. They lived their tiny lives, burrowed through silt that fused their corpses into apparently eternal solidity, although now they crumble at our touch or the caress of a raindrop. Everything rots eventually.

Even the forbidding cliffs on which they stand are being worn away by the swelling of tides, the sucking and lapping of every wave against their headlands and shoals, the faintest kiss of spume.

Bass Rock is pocked and seamed, seemingly tainted by the stench of guano and the evil of our doings: yet look again and human activity is ... nothing. We are a flicker of shadow on its skin. It rose from the earth's mantle, a cataclysm of infernal heat, shrieking, tortured fire and water, explosions of lava and steam all unheard, unseen, titanic forces so distant that only a stubby relic pokes today from the surf.

The volcanic forges slowed and stilled when the moon was young. Acid rain swept them clean when our ancestors dreamed of swinging through trees.

Creatures evolved and extinguished before we rubbed sticks together, nibbled lichen from the first frail layer of soil, then fled before towering ice sheets that ground dead pyroclastic rivers to grit.

Now gulls and gannets gabble and huddle in its creases, parents squabble on the curves of Canty Bay, and children make copycat castles on pretty beaches made from exoskeletal remains.

It can spark visceral terror, that epiphany, that your life is an infinitesimal speck in, well, infinity. Or acceptance. This palimpsest is unfinished. The tapestry will be patched and rewoven over and again. We are a moment in passing, not the ending. We will be stitched over, worn away, lost in folds and faded seams, our bones perished to dust and our fortresses flown like frayed cobwebs on the breeze.

Stray fossils of us will be flicked and discarded by whatever comes after us, as we now skim pebbles across rockpools. Even storms will be silenced, dying with the earth. The sun will gather in its errant children from the void and all that seemed unending will cease.

My spirit's turmoil - or comfort - is to know that there is no emotion behind the death of it all. We know evil, we do evil, but time, tide, light and darkness, they just... are.

We cannot foist notions of spite or hate on eternity. Neither love. Nor mercy. There is no reason why we live to die, other than this is what Being is. Entropy. Or God.

I lie on the grass at Tantallon, listening to the skylark's paean to existence. He sings.

I am strong, I fly high, I shout my
need to live, to feed, to fuck, to have power in
my little world.
I am singing to another day free from death,
defying time's gravity.

And I chew a grass stem in the shade of the ramparts and think, aren't we all.

TENDERNESS &
THE DISTANCE

E.E Benson

Erica Benson is a conservation and environmental scientist.

She was brought up in the Yorkshire Dales where she first developed her love of natural history and has lived in rural Fife for almost thirty years.

Her non-fiction academic writing career spans more than four decades, during which time her participation in international conservation projects provided the opportunity to work and publish in many regions of the world.

Erica retired early from professional life to focus on exploring nature and watching wildlife in Scotland and beyond, these experiences prompted her to 'have a go' at nature writing, Haiku and Ecofiction. Erica is finding her new creative writing endeavours both daunting and exhilarating.

An Ode to the Seasons

Winter

Hare & Eagle

soft snowflakes collapse
on a mountain hare's eyelash
golden eagle blinks

blizzards cut through fur
whiteout hare hides out of sight
golden eagle waits

clouds build drifting snow
mountain hare sleeps camouflaged
golden eagle soars

melting snow reveals
old mountain hare quivering
golden eagle eats

Red Squirrel

Scots pine needles stir
tree branch bothy hides a tail
dry leaves twigs grass moss

bleak start bitter day
red squirrel flit, flitters, flits
between dry drey dens

darting pointy ears
quickening in conifers
ancient pines stand watch

acorns mushrooms bark
pine seed caches are secured
squirreled away cafe

Spring

Hawthorn

green man is unmasked
the world tree is waking up
it is the fifth month

day length detonates
the elemental green fuse
hawthorn smokes pale leaves

hedgerows fizz with scent
unwisely forbidden plant
ill fated plague bloom

the cloth clout is cast
resetting growing life lines
May flowers break bud

Fox Gloves

she fox cub follows
pollen powdered velvet bee
snout in nectary

fox cub licks her fur
brother cocks his pointed ears
golden plover pipes

green cubs grow in dew
clever little explorers
sniffing every thing

rain does not stop play
chasing moonshine in puddles
foxes wear pink gloves

Summer

Heather Honey

August flowering
pollinators orbiting
wind fertilizing

all shades of heather
bombus buzzes pollen dust
mountains grow shadows

quantum light creates
a living constellation
summer particles

blazing with bee life
the alchemy of honey
stigma stamen style

Bats & Midges

midsummer night bats
dream of warm air maneuvers
over river space

midsummer night bats
dream of hunting water stars
echolocation

midsummer night bats
dream of whirring antennae
sonar sensing traps

midsummer night bats
dream of blood sunset feasting
bane of midges slain

Autumn

Red Deer

November's cold mists
hide high mountain browsing hinds
rival stags bellow

roaring ricochets
booming over mountain peaks
challengers reply

pointed antlers clash
stags spar fight push lock twist thrash
age predicts a loss

frenzied mad-eyed stag
muscle sinew bone skull cleaved
mouth foams floods of blood

Fly Agaric

soft mycelia
travel on the underground
linking tree mile roots

red cap spotted white
the world of woodland helpers
fragile fungal fruit

Autumn's mycospheres
decode decomposition
and build new forests

toadstool DNA
Amanita explodes spores
trillions dispersed

Wendy Grosvenor

Wendy is interested in sensory, physical experiences, the weight and heft of a sound, the history of a sound in the air and the fabric of a place. She is also obsessed with the sensory, bodily connection that we have with our planet. Her mediums are space, spoken and unspoken words, and sound.

She works to narrate a connection – and to note a disconnection – through deep listening, sensory practice, video and oral gesture.

Her work asks for a reflection, through focus of attention.

Catch her on YouTube at Wendy Grosvenor Art

My Words

How do my words feel in
your mouth?
Are they smooth, grey,
rounded
Stones, sucked and held?
Will they jar or crack a tooth? Fill a throat,
choke, grind?

Are they like a woolly cloth, so absorbent
that they stuff the mouth cavity, sucking
all moisture with them, leaving a dry
inability to speak?

Are they grainy, like sand shifting, sliding
away on the tongue; breaking apart from a
large, claggy clump?

Do they feel slippery? Filling your mouth
with juices? Don't swallow, keep swilling
them around inside.

Will your mouth feel empty, once you spit
them out?

There is a silence in winter

There is a silence in winter.
A folding over; a holding down.

There is containment by every locutor
In sound struck dumb through an empty
space.

Strangled by cold air.
A journey made slow as it tries to speak.

I want this to be the same silence that I can
hear
In between two musical notes.

But winter has lost its tongue.

Inside

INSIDE. MOVING THROUGH. INSIDE you feel safe. You are always with someone, you are not often alone.

Time feels palpable. You can touch it. It clings to your face and you breathe it in. When you move through the building it is always with someone.

Movement is slow, like the time, like treacle. He unlocks the door with a bunch of large metal keys. You both move through. He locks the door with the keys.

You move on. He unlocks another door with a bunch of large metal keys, you both move through. He locks the door with the keys. It all takes such a long time and repeats and repeats and repeats.

INSIDE it is calm. There is very little sound. Noise and conversation hang heavy, suspended in the thixotropic void.

When I meet the inmates they all seem so young, so ordinary so small. My son, my brother, my friend, my partner.

'Don't engage with the prisoners. Yes, be friendly, but be careful what you say.' They can find out your entire history and personal set up by stitching together tiny threads and patches of random conversation.

The air, space and place feel heavier and more closed in. More doors, more keys. The clunk and thud of a closing.

'Do you know what the boys enjoy doing the most? says a Warden, 'they love sewing. Stitching together sample shapes of teddy bears, dogs, cats, with big stitches'.

I think ....there is a latent anger - a secret malevolency in sharp, stabbed stitching..... a meditative ritual.

'It creates for the inmates a sense of connection with their home, their partners, their children', says the Warden.

Why would you ever want to leave such a safe, secure, benign environment, I wonder?

OUTSIDE the air is fresh, breezy, uncontained, and the spring sunshine bouncing off the high brick wall feels light and special upon my face.

8d Press started life in Australia back in 1994 as a small literary press, publishing sensory and erotic short prose poetry pieces plus an anthology. Its books were hand-designed and made in an era before the internet. As a small press we have released eight chapbooks which we sell on various online platforms. These are delicately produced and designed physical books - pocket-sized - that offer a 'taste' of the sensory for those broad-minded of souls. LUCENT - An ode to Nan Shepherd's *The Living Mountain* - is 8d Press's first Scottish-based book.

Our mission statement is:

We love beautiful physical things, we adore local craftsmanship and we adore the 'local', the 'real' and the 'rare'. We only ever print limited edition books. All of our books are printed in 60 and 500 copy projects and we never, ever produce our versions in ebooks. For us human stories are everything and the writings we publish always reflect the human and the physical. Every book we produce is numbered and dated by hand by us in our studio in Dunfermline, Fife Scotland.

Our chapbooks and books can be bought from us online at www.8dpress.co.uk but first always check your local independent bookshop and request our books from them, using our ISBNs. Thank you.

Support Your Independent Bookseller.

Use the following pages to pen your own unique story. Everyone has a story in them. Start writing yours here.

80/500
June 2021